Stage 2

Professor Boffin's Umbrella

Longman Structural Readers

L.G. Alexander

Illustrated by Bailey Pettengell Design Ltd

Mrs Boffin is looking out of the window. Professor Boffin is sitting on a chair. He is reading. "Don't read today, dear," Mrs Boffin says. "It's a nice day. We can go for a walk in the park." "Yes, dear," the Professor says.

"Put on your coat," Mrs Boffin says. "Take your umbrella, too. There are some clouds in the sky." "Where's my umbrella, dear?" "Here," Mrs Boffin says and she gives it to him. "I don't like this umbrella. It's very old."

Now they are walking in the park. Mrs Boffin is looking at the sky. It isn't blue now. It's black! "Look at those clouds," she says. "It's going to rain. Open your umbrella, dear. Please be quick! It's going to rain heavily!"

2

Now it's raining heavily. Professor Boffin has opened his umbrella and Mrs Boffin is looking at it. "This umbrella's full of holes," she says. "You need a new umbrella, dear. You must buy a new umbrella!"

Now they are home. Their clothes are very wet. "Look at my hair," Mrs Boffin says. "It's very wet. And look at my clothes! They're full of water!" But the Professor isn't listening. He's thinking.

Now Professor Boffin is holding his umbrella and is looking at it. "What are you doing with that umbrella?" Mrs Boffin asks. "I'm thinking," he says. "This umbrella's old. I must make a new umbrella. A special umbrella."

3

Professor Boffin goes to his work-room. He stays there for ten hours. He isn't thinking now. He is working hard. He's making a new umbrella. It isn't an ordinary umbrella. It's a special umbrella. "I must test it," he says.

It is very dark now. Mrs Boffin is asleep, but the Professor is going out. It's not raining, but he's holding his special umbrella. He's going to test it. There's a policeman in the street, but the Professor doesn't see him.

Professor Boffin opens his umbrella and goes up into the air. He flies over his house. "This umbrella's very good," he thinks. "I can fly to the moon and stars." The policeman in the street looks up. "What's that?" he cries.

"I've tested the umbrella and I must return to the ground," Professor Boffin thinks. He is returning to the ground now and the policeman is watching him. "What are you doing? Where are you going?" the policeman calls.

The Professor is on the ground and the policeman is talking to him. The policeman is holding a pen and a little book. "What's your name?" he asks.
"Boffin," the Professor says.
The policeman writes in his book.

The policeman looks at the umbrella. "What's this?" he asks.
"An umbrella," the Professor says, "an ordinary umbrella."
"What are you doing with it?"
"I'm testing it."
"But it isn't raining!"

"Where do you live?" the policeman asks.
"Here," the Professor says. "I'm going to bed now. Good night."
"Good night," the policeman says. "I can't understand it," he thinks. "This is very strange!"

It is morning. Professor and Mrs Boffin are eating their breakfast.
"Did you make a new umbrella?" Mrs Boffin asks.
"Yes, dear," the Professor says.
"You must take it with you," she says. "It's going to rain today."

Professor Boffin is leaving home. He's wearing his hat and carrying his umbrella. "That's a nice umbrella," Mrs Boffin says. "It will rain today, so you can test it."
"Yes dear. Goodbye."
"Goodbye, dear," Mrs Boffin says.

Professor Boffin hasn't gone to work today. He is in the country. He's standing in a quiet field. "Now I can test my umbrella very well," the Professor thinks. "I can fly to the moon." He opens the umbrella and flies into the air.

Professor Boffin is flying over the clouds now. "It's very nice up here," he thinks. "The sky's blue and there aren't any clouds over my head." Then he sees a jet aircraft. "There's a jet!" he says. "I can wave to the pilots."

The jet is near the Professor now. "Look!" the first pilot cries. "What's that? Is it a bird?" "No!" the second pilot says. "It's a man. He's holding an umbrella and waving to us!" "A man!" the first pilot cries.

7

Professor Boffin is in space now. The sky is black and the stars are shining. The moon is shining, too. It is very big. Professor Boffin is flying towards it. "This umbrella's very good, but it never rains up here!" he thinks.

8

This rocket is flying to the moon, too. There are two astronauts in the rocket. There is a space station on the moon and the men are flying towards it. "We are very near the moon now," the first astronaut says.

"Yes," the second astronaut says. "The moon is 25,000 miles away now. We'll be there for lunch."
"Good!" the first astronaut answers. "I didn't have time for breakfast this morning. I want a good lunch. Don't you?"

Suddenly, the first astronaut sees Professor Boffin. "That's strange, Charlie!" he cries. "I can't understand it. Look at that man! He's wearing a hat and holding an umbrella. He's flying through space!"

The second astronaut looks through the window. "He's waving to us," he says. "Wave to him, Bill." The astronauts are waving to the Professor and he is waving to them.
"Follow him, Charlie," Bill says. "Quick! He's going to the moon."

"I can't follow him," Charlie says. "He's moving very quickly. I can't see him now. He's far away." Professor Boffin has passed the rocket now. He's flying very quickly. He's flying at 180,000 miles a second!

Now Professor Boffin is flying over the moon. He can see the white mountains. He can see the space station, too. There are some astronauts near the station. The Professor isn't far away, but the astronauts haven't seen him yet.

10

Two astronauts are talking. "What's the time?" the first man asks.
"It's 12 o'clock. Why?"
"Because Bill and Charlie will come here today. They're going to have lunch with us. They'll be here at 12.30."

Suddenly, the first astronaut sees the Professor. "Look at that, Tom!" he cries. "It's not a rocket. What is it?"
"I don't know," Tom says. "Isn't it a man? He's holding an umbrella and he's raising his hat!"

The astronauts are still watching the Professor, but he isn't coming down. "I won't go to the moon," he thinks. "I'll fly through space and I'll go to the stars." Professor Boffin raises his umbrella and moves away.

The astronauts on the moon are still looking at the Professor. "Is he coming down to the moon?" the first astronaut asks. "No," the second man says. "Look! He's flying up to the stars. His umbrella is like a rocket!"

"Quick! We must follow him!" the first astronaut says. "We can't do that," the second man says. "He's very far away. He's flying at 180,000 miles a second. Our rocket can't fly like that. It's very slow."

Professor Boffin is looking down. He can see the moon and he can see the earth. The moon looks small and the earth looks small, too. "Mrs Boffin will like this umbrella," he thinks. "It isn't full of holes. It's like a rocket!"

The Professor can't see the earth and the moon now. They are far away. He is looking at a star. It is shining in space. The name of the star is Tau Ceti. "That's Tau Ceti," Professor Boffin thinks. "I can go there."

Professor Boffin is still flying, but he's very tired. "I'm very tired," he thinks. "I must sleep." He shuts his eyes and goes to sleep. He is still holding his umbrella and is still flying through space—but he's asleep!

Professor Boffin isn't asleep now. He's looking at his watch. "It's 4.30," he thinks. "Where am I? I can't see the moon or the earth and I can't see Tau Ceti. Oh dear! I've lost my way. I must go back to the earth!"

The Professor is looking round. "Where's the earth?" he asks. "Oh dear! What will Mrs Boffin say? She won't like my umbrella now. I can't find the earth. I've lost my way and I don't want to stay up here. It's not very nice."

Suddenly, Professor Boffin sees a strange thing in the sky. It's very small and very far away. "What's that?" he thinks. "It's shining, but it isn't a star. It's moving through space very quickly. It's coming towards me!"

13

"It looks like a saucer!" he thinks. "It's a flying saucer. It's coming towards me and it looks very big now. I must fly towards it, too. The creatures in the saucer can help me. I shall say, 'I've lost my way'."

14

The flying saucer has stopped over Professor Boffin's head. He is looking up at it and he is waving his hat. He can see a ladder. The ladder is under the flying saucer. "I can climb up that ladder," he thinks.

He has shut his umbrella now and is climbing up the ladder. The door under the saucer is opening. There is a dark hole under the saucer. The Professor will go through the dark hole. He will climb into the flying saucer.

Professor Boffin is in the saucer now. He can see two strange creatures. Their heads and their bodies are green. They are very short and they have big black eyes. The creatures are looking at the Professor and his umbrella.

"Good afternoon," Professor Boffin says and raises his hat. The creatures do not speak. They watch the professor and they look at his hat. "These creatures don't understand English," the Professor thinks. "What can I do?"

Now the Professor is holding a map of the sky. He is pointing at the earth on the map. The creatures are looking at the map. "I come from the planet, Earth," the Professor says and he points at it. "The planet, Earth."

15

"The planet, Earth!" the green creatures cry. "We often go there. We went there yesterday." "Do you speak English?" the Professor asks.
"Yes, we speak English well," they say. "We learnt it at school."

"The earth is a nice place for a picnic," the green creatures say. We had a picnic there yesterday." "I must give you my name and address," the Professor says and he writes his name and address on a piece of paper.

The green creatures look at the piece of paper. "Niffob," they say. "Your name's Niffob." "No, Boffin," the Professor says. "Niffob!" the creatures say. "We always read backwards. We shall call you Niffob."

16

"My name's Grorg. And my name's Tobbot," the creatures say. "You can read our names backwards, too, Niffob." Grorg is writing their names on a piece of paper. Tobbot is looking at the Professor's umbrella.

"What's this?" Tobbot asks and he points at the umbrella. "An umbrella," the Professor says, "but it isn't an ordinary umbrella. It's a special umbrella." "I don't understand," Tobbot says. "Is it an umbrella, or isn't it?"

"It's like a saucer," the Professor says. "You open it and then you can fly through space." "I must test it, Niffob," Tobbot says. "Give it to me. Open the door, Grorg. I'm going to test Niffob's umbrella-saucer."

The saucer has stopped in space. Tobbot has gone through the door and has climbed down the ladder. He has opened Professor Boffin's umbrella. Now he is flying round the saucer. The umbrella flies very well and Tobbot looks happy.

18

Tobbot has returned to the saucer.
"It's a good saucer, Niffob," he says and he gives the umbrella to the Professor. Grorg is looking at the map of the sky.
"Tell me, Niffob," Grorg says.
"Where are you going?"

"I went to the moon."
"Which moon?" Tobbot asks.
"Our moon. The earth moon."
"Oh, yes," Grorg says. "We know that place. It's not a very nice place. We never go there for picnics, do we Tobbot?"

"Then I wanted to go to Tau Ceti, but I went to sleep."
"Sleep?" Tobbot says. "We never sleep. That's a bad habit, Niffob. It's a very bad habit!"
"Tau Ceti?" Grorg says. "That star is our sun."

"Yes," Tobbot says. "We live on the planet, Ozo. It goes round Tau Ceti. It's a nice place. Are you going there now, Niffob?"
"No," the Professor says. "I don't want to go to Ozo. I've lost my way. I want to go home."

"We can take you home," Grorg says. "We know the way very well. You'll like Ozo. You can stay with us."
"You don't understand," the Professor says. "I want to go to the earth."
"We'll take you," Tobbot says.

Tobbot touches a big red button in the saucer. The word EARTH is on the button. Suddenly, the saucer goes very quickly. It goes at 186,000 miles a second. "We are going to earth now," Tobbot calls. "Do you hear me?"

The Professor doesn't hear Tobbot. He is very tired. He is sleeping.
"Niffob!" Grorg cries.
"What? What? I'm dreaming!"
"Remember! You mustn't sleep and dream," Grorg says. "It's a very bad habit. You have bad habits!"

The saucer is flying through space. The earth is far away, but the saucer is moving very quickly. There are big lights round the saucer. They are shining in the black sky. The saucer looks like a big star in the sky.

Mrs Boffin is going to bed. "What's the time?" she says. "Oh dear! It's eleven o'clock. Professor Boffin hasn't come home yet. I can't wait for him. I must go to bed now. I'm tired. I must go to sleep."

It's very dark in the streets. The people are sleeping, but there are some men in the park. They are standing on a hill. They have a telescope and are looking at the sky. They are looking at the moon, the planets and the stars.

"Jim! Jim!" the man with the telescope calls. "Look at this. It's very strange!" Jim looks through the telescope. "Yes," he cries, "it *is* strange! It isn't a planet or a star. It's moving very quickly."

"It's a flying saucer!" he cries. "I can see it very well. It's round and there are lights round it. It's near the moon now, but it isn't going to the moon. It's moving towards the earth. It's going to come here!"

"Give me the telescope, Jim!" his friend cries. He looks through it. "Yes," he says. "I can see the saucer, too." "A flying saucer! A flying saucer!" Jim cries. "There's a flying saucer in the sky!"

Some people in the park hear him and they run towards the hill. They can see the saucer, too. They don't need a telescope now. They can see the saucer very well without a telescope. It's very big. It's near the earth.

"We're over the earth now," Tobbot says. "Where do you want to go, Niffob? America? Africa? Asia? Europe?"

"England!" the Professor says.

"England?" Grorg says. "Where's that? I don't know that place."

"Here!" the Professor says and he points at the map. "England's a country in Europe."

"I know England," Tobbot says. "We went there for a picnic two years ago, but we didn't stay there. Some people saw us."

"Yes, I remember now," Grorg says. "They had a telescope and they saw us. We can't go to England again, Niffob. We'll take you to China. That's a nice place."

"I don't want to go to China. I want to go home, to England!"

23

"Then we'll drop you over England and you can return with your umbrella," Tobbot says. "Where do you want to go?" "Here," the Professor says. "My home is here. You can drop me over my home and I'll fly down."

24

"We're near your home now, Niffob," Grorg says. "Open the door, Tobbot and put out the ladder. Niffob can climb down the ladder. Then he can jump." Tobbot opens the door and puts out the ladder for the Professor.

"Goodbye, my friends," Professor Boffin calls, "and thank you!" "Goodbye Niffob," Grorg and Tobbot call. "Don't drop your umbrella. We'll come to your country for a picnic one day. Goodbye! And don't lose your way."

There are twenty people on the hill now. They can see the big flying saucer. It has stopped over the hill. They can see a creature on the ladder. The "creature" is Professor Boffin, but the people don't know this!

"Look!" Jim cries. "A strange creature is jumping out of the saucer. It's coming here. Oh dear! What can we do? Call a policeman quickly. The creature is coming down, but the saucer is moving away from the earth."

It's dark again now. The saucer has gone, but the men on the hill are watching Professor Boffin. The Professor is coming down with his umbrella. There is a policeman on the hill. He is watching the Professor, too!

Professor Boffin is flying over the town now. He can see the streets and the park. "I can land in the park," he thinks. "Then that policeman won't see me and won't ask me questions. I didn't like that policeman!"

The Professor is flying over the trees in the park. "I'll land under those trees," he thinks. "It's quiet there. Then I'll walk home. What's the time?" He looks at his watch. "It's one o'clock," he says.

Professor Boffin is landing now, but suddenly his umbrella touches a branch. The branch holds the umbrella and it can't go down! The Professor looks down. "I can't move!" he cries. "I can't fly to the ground. Help! Help!"

The people are running down the hill. "Where did the creature land?" they cry. "We must find him."
"There!" the policeman says. "Quick! Follow me!"
The people are following the policeman down the hill.

Now they are walking through the trees. "Where is this creature?" Jim asks. "It's very quiet here."
"Listen!" the policeman cries. The people stop and listen.
"Help!" Professor Boffin cries. "I'm on this branch."

"Did you hear that?" the policeman asks. "This creature is calling us. Listen!"
"Help! Help!" the Professor cries.
"Quick! Follow me!" the policeman says and he points to a tree.
"The sound is coming from there."

Now the people are standing under the tree. They are looking up at Professor Boffin. "I'll speak to this creature," the policeman says: "Stay here. Don't go near it. I'll take the creature to the police-station."

28

"What are you doing up there?" the policeman calls. "The branches are holding my umbrella and I can't come down," the Professor says. "Please don't stand there. Help me!" The policeman climbs the tree.

Now the policeman is bringing Professor Boffin down. He is carrying him on his back. "This creature speaks English," Jim says. "It comes from far away and it speaks English! It's a very strange creature!"

The policeman and the Professor are standing on the ground now. The people are standing round them. They aren't standing near the Professor, but they are watching him. The policeman is holding a pencil and a little book.

"Now," the policeman says. "What's your name please?" "Niffob," the Professor says. "Niffob?" the policeman asks. "No! Not Niffob. Boffin! My name's Boffin. You know me. Don't you remember me?"

The policeman looks at the Professor. "Boffin!" he cries. "Yes, I remember you. You're the man with the umbrella. What are you doing here?" "I went for a walk and then I climbed a tree. I wanted to see the stars."

"But the saucer! We saw a saucer," the people say. "You came out of a flying saucer!" "No!" the Professor says. "I live here. This policeman knows me. I'm Professor Boffin. There wasn't a saucer. I didn't see it."

"Are we dreaming?" the people ask.
"I don't know," the policeman says. "But I know one thing. This man isn't a strange creature. He lives near here and his name is Boffin. I know that. You can go home now, Professor."

Professor Boffin arrives home. "Mrs Boffin is sleeping now," he thinks. "That's a bad habit! But it's a very nice habit, too. I'm tired. I want to go to sleep now." He opens his front door and goes into the house quietly.

t is morning. Mrs Boffin is ooking out of the window. The Professor is reading. "You came home late yesterday, dear." "Yes," the Professor answers. "I was with Grorg and Tobbot." "Who?" Mrs Boffin asks.

"Some friends," the Professor says.
"Oh yes," Mrs Boffin answers. "We can go for a walk today. It's a nice day, but take your new umbrella. I can see some clouds in the sky. It's going to rain heavily."

They are walking in the park, but it's raining heavily. "Look at your new umbrella," Mrs Boffin says. "It's full of holes. It's not a very good umbrella."
"Yes, dear," the Professor says. "It isn't very good—now!"

A. Read these sentences:
The Professor is going to open his umbrella.
Now he has opened his umbrella.
You do the same. Begin each sentence with **Now**:
1. The Professor is going to test it.
2. The flying saucer is going to stop.
3. The Professor is going to go through the door.
4. The Professor is going to climb down the ladder.
5. The flying saucer is going to land.
6. The Professor is going to jump out.
7. The people are going to call a policeman.
8. The Professor is going to shut his umbrella.
9. The policeman is going to write it in his book.
10. Mrs Boffin is going to go to sleep.

B. Read these sentences:
Professor Boffin is going to open his umbrella.
Now he is opening his umbrella.
You do the same. Begin each sentence with **Now**:
1. Mrs Boffin is going to look out of the window.
2. The Professor is going to read.
3. It's going to rain heavily.
4. The policeman is going to talk to him.
5. The Professor is going to put on his hat.
6. The pilots are going to wave to him.
7. The astronauts are going to fly to the moon.
8. The Professor is going to raise his hat.
9. The people are going to watch the flying saucer.
10. Jim is going to look through the telescope.

C. Read these sentences:
We often go there.
We went there yesterday.
Now write these sentences again. Your sentences must end with **yesterday**:
1. It often rains.
2. He often comes here.
3. We often see him.
4. I often lose my way.
5. He often goes for a walk.
6. She often climbs this tree.
7. The pilot often waves to us.
8. They often stay at our house.
9. They often walk in the park.
10. She often arrives at four o'clock.
11. We often have a picnic.
12. She often tells us a story.

D. Finish these sentences. Put in the words
up, of, from, through, in, to or *on:*
1. He can see some men _____ the moon.
2. It is moving away _____ the earth.
3. There are some clouds _____ the sky.
4. "Put _____ your coat," she says.
5. This umbrella is full _____ holes.
6. There is a policeman _____ the street.
7. He's waving _____ us.
8. He's looking _____ the telescope.
9. The rocket is flying _____ the moon.
10. I can climb _____ that ladder.

32